Topic 1

Issues and debates in psychology

Item 1 Gender and culture in psychology

Cultural bias

Culture can be defined as 'the beliefs, attitudes, social and child-rearing practices etc.' that people of a group share and that distinguishes one group from other groups.

Ethnocentrism

Ethnocentrism is the effect that your own cultural perspective has on the way you perceive other cultures and people from other cultures. For example, it is ethnocentric to assume that what is true of our culture is also true of other cultures.

Emic or etic

Emic constructs are traits that are specific to a certain culture (e.g. monogamy in Western culture). Etic constructs are universal traits that can be found across cultures (e.g. family). In the history of psychology, emic (culturally specific) constructs have been assumed to be etic. For example, research into conformity, relationships and diagnosing psychological disorders.

Individualistic or collectivist cultures

In individualistic cultures, one's identity is defined by personal characteristics, independence and achievements. In collectivist cultures, identity is defined by collective achievements and interdependence.

Cultural relativism

Cultural relativism is the view that beliefs, customs and ethics are relative to the individual within his or her own social context. In other words, what is considered moral in one society may be considered immoral in another, and, since no universal standard of morality exists, no one has the right to judge the customs of another society. Cultural relativists believe that all cultures are of equal value.

Bias in psychological research

Temporal bias

All cultures changes over time. For example, in the 1950s British culture was very different (e.g. homosexuality was seen as a mental illness).

Research and sample bias

Problems may arise because of translation, and also because, although in cross-cultural research samples may be taken from similar groups (e.g. students), the social backgrounds and life experiences of the participants from different cultures may be very different.

Alpha and beta bias

- **Alpha bias.** When alpha bias occurs, research tends to emphasise and over exaggerate differences between cultures (or between genders).
- **Beta bias.** When beta bias occurs, research tends to minimise or ignore differences between cultures (and genders). Examples of beta bias include Kohlberg's theory of universal stages of moral development and evolutionary theories of behaviour where men are portrayed as hunting and women looking after children.

The effect of ethnocentrism and alpha and/or beta bias is to create and perpetuate stereotypes and to make cultures (and genders) seem more different (or more similar) than they are.

Gender bias: androcentrism

Androcentrism occurs when male views and behaviour are viewed as 'the norm' and used to explain both male and female behaviour. Androcentrism also occurs when female behaviour is different from male behaviour and is construed as abnormal or inferior because it is different. Examples of androcentric psychology are Bowlby's research into attachment and maternal care that suggested women should stay at home and care for children and Freud suggesting that women suffered from 'penis envy'.

Read Item 1 and your textbook.

1 a Write a definition of ethnocentrism.

....
....
....
....
....

b When considering the characteristics of different cultures what is the difference between emic and etic constructs?

....
....
....
....
....
....
....

c When undertaking research into gender, what is the difference between alpha bias and beta bias?

....
....
....
....
....
....
....

d Give an example of research which involved a biased sample of students.

....
....

e Give an example of research which involved an androcentric sample.

....
....

f Give an example of a study that may involve temporal bias.

....
....

Item 2 Free will and determinism

Most people feel that they have free will to make choices and that their behaviour is not determined for them but is the product of their own volition. However, this position creates difficulties for scientific research which assumes causal and deterministic relationships.

- **Hard determinism** suggests behaviour is caused by genetic factors.
- Some psychologists see the source of determinism as being outside the individual, a position known as environmental determinism. For example, Bandura (1961) showed that children with violent parents will in turn become violent parents through observation and imitation.
- The term **soft determinism** is often used to describe situations in which people do have a choice, but their behaviour is subject to some form of biological or environmental pressure.
- **Psychic determinism** is the type of determinism that suggests all mental processes are determined by the unconscious or pre-existing mental complexes.

Item 3 The nature–nurture debate

To what extent is any behaviour the result of your genetic code (nature — the genes you inherit) or due to your life experiences (nurture — your parents, your upbringing, your experiences generally)? This debate is especially relevant in the areas of language, aggression, gender and dysfunctional behaviour.

Some research explains behaviour as being caused by nature (e.g. ageing). For example, Piaget suggests that children's thought processes change at predetermined ages. Other research, for example Bandura, demonstrates that behaviour is not innate and that children who observe adult role models behaving aggressively learn from what they see and imitate aggressive actions. Of course, nature and nurture interact and much research sees nature as 'potential' which is modified by nurture.

Item 4 Holism and reductionism

Levels of explanation for behaviour

The four levels of explanation for behaviour are as follows:

- The **biological level** of explanation focuses on the biological and chemical processes underlying behaviour. For example, the role played by genes or hormones in aggression.
- The **basic processes** level of explanation focuses on the psychological (e.g. cognitive) processes that are universal across humans. For example, the thoughts and emotions involved in aggression.
- The **person level** of explanation focuses on individual differences in behaviour. For example, personality differences in aggressive people.
- The **sociocultural level** of explanation focuses on the influence of other people on behaviour by studying behaviour in social and cultural contexts. For example, how being in a crowd influences whether or not people behave aggressively.

Reductionism

Reductionism is the principle of analysing complex things into simple constituents or the use of simple principles, for example explaining complex human behaviour in terms of simplistic single factor causes, such as inherited genes. Science is reductionist because, to find out how things work, it studies parts rather than whole entities. Reductionist hypotheses are easier to test and they can be 'proven' (or not). However, reductionist and simplistic explanations for behaviour may prevent further attempts to find more complex but less clear-cut explanations.

Note: Many psychological accounts which are reductionist are also deterministic.

Holism

Holism is the principal that the behaviour of the 'whole system' cannot be explained in terms of the 'sum' of the behaviour of all of the different parts. Although simple explanations are appropriate in some situations, simple explanations rarely explain the richness of human experience and prevent the search for more complex answers.

Item 5 Idiographic and nomothetic approaches

- The term **nomothetic** comes from the Greek word 'nomos' meaning 'law'. Psychologists who take a nomothetic approach to psychological investigation study groups to make generalisations about behaviour.
- The term **idiographic** comes from the Greek word 'idios' meaning 'own'. Psychologists who take an ideographic approach to psychological investigation want to discover what makes each of us unique.

Experimental and other quantitative methods are favoured from a nomothetic point of view. Case studies and other qualitative methods are idiographic. Nomothetic, experimental research enables the development of general laws of behaviour. Idiographic, qualitative research provides a more complete (holistic) understanding of an individual's behaviour.

Behaviourist, cognitive and biological approaches tend to take a nomothetic approach and focus on establishing generalisations. Humanistic approaches are interested in the individual and are thus idiographic. The psychodynamic approach is arguably idiographic because although Freud suggests that the structure of the unconscious mind is common to everyone, each patient's individual problems arise from unique childhood experience.

Item 6 Ethical implications of research

Ethics in research

Ethical issues may arise because of a conflict of interest between the researcher and the researched. The researcher may wish to collect in-depth high quality data and may be tempted to consider unethical research practice in order to try to obtain data.

Ethical risks and responsibilities

Researchers need to consider the potential physical or psychological risks to participants and are responsible for ensuring that the level of risk is minimised and that participants are fully aware of any risk before they agree to participate. The risks may be physical or psychological arising from discussion of sensitive topics, stirring painful memories, or disclosure of personal information. Ethical issues relate especially to interview methods, where participants may be encouraged to disclose personal information, but ethical issues arise in all research involving human participants.

Basic principles of ethical research

- **Informed consent.** There should be informed consent from participants before they take part.
- **No pressure on individuals to participate.** Incentives to take part should generally not be provided.
- **Respect individual autonomy.** Even when people have given consent to participate they must be made aware that they are free to withdraw from the study at any time, without giving a reason.
- **Avoid causing harm.** The duty of the researcher is not to cause harm.
- **Maintain anonymity and confidentiality.** Making data 'anonymous'.
- **Research with vulnerable groups.** Care is needed in research with young children, and with people who are ill, or recently bereaved or others who may be vulnerable.
- **Socially sensitive research.** There is increasing research interest in 'sensitive' social issues such as sexuality or child abuse. Any topic could potentially be seen to be sensitive and ethical issues may arise when in-depth interviews/questionnaires are used that may unleash painful emotions and memories in participants.

Read Items 2-6 and your textbook.

2 a Answer TRUE or FALSE to the following questions.

    i The physiological approach is reductionist. _____

    ii The behaviourist approach is not deterministic. _____

    iii The psychodynamic approach suggests people have free will. _____

    iv The cognitive approach is deterministic. _____

    v The behaviourist approach gives a nature explanation for behaviour. _____

    vi The physiological approach gives a nature explanation for behaviour. _____

b What word is used to describe 'psychologists who study groups of people and formulate general laws'?

....

c List one nomothetic example AND one idiographic example in psychological research or theory.

....

....

....

....

d Explain the difference between biological determinism and environmental determinism.

....

....

....

....

....

....

....

....

e Which of the four levels of explanation is used by the psychodynamic approach?

....

....

....

f Which of the four levels of explanation is used by the physiological approach?

....

....

....

g Outline what is meant by reductionism.

....

....

....

....

....

....

h Explain whether experimental research into memory by cognitive psychologists is nomothetic or idiographic.

....

....

....

....

....

....

i In a study of bullying in schools, researchers went to ABC secondary school and interviewed 50 girls and boys aged 12. They then classified each child according to whether they were 'a bully', 'bullied' or 'neither'. They concluded that the school's anti-bullying policy was not effective as 20% of the children said they had been bullied or involved in bullying.

   Explain what is meant by 'socially sensitive research' and suggest why this research can be seen as socially sensitive.

....

....

....

....

....

....

....

....

....

....

....

....

....

Exam-style questions

3 **a** Which of the following approaches is most likely to be described as environmental determinism? `1 mark`

Circle the letter of the answer that you think is correct.

A Biological approach

B Behaviourist approach

C Psychodynamic approach

D Social approach

b A psychologist researching friendship patterns recruited 50 female participants and asked them to complete a questionnaire. Which of the following biases is not demonstrated by this research? `1 mark`

Circle the letter of the answer that you think is correct.

A Gender bias

B Androcentric bias

C Beta bias

c Name two types of reductionism in psychology. `2 marks`

....

....

d In psychological research, what is the difference between alpha bias and beta bias? `2 marks`

....

....

....

....

....

....

....

....

e Outline what psychologists mean by determinism. `2 marks`

....

....

....

....

....

....

....

f   Discuss the usefulness of reductionist explanations in psychology.   6 marks

....

....

....

....

....

....

....

....

....

....

g   Outline the difference between the person level explanation and the sociocultural
    level explanation for behaviour.   4 marks

....

....

....

....

....

....

h   Discuss the usefulness of a sociocultural explanation for behaviour.   6 marks

....

....

....

....

....

....

....

....

....

Topic 2

Relationships

Item 1 Evolutionary explanations

Research into partner preferences looks at factors that determine why we are attracted to others. Evolutionary psychologists propose that mate choice is unconsciously guided by cues that indicate some survival advantage for offspring and that because parental investment in reproduction is different for males and females, mate choice cues are different for males and females.

Sexual selection and human reproductive behaviour

Parental investment

Human females invest a great deal of time and energy in their offspring. A baby is helpless, dependent on the mother at birth, and requires intensive rearing so a female has relatively few offspring and requires a mate who is willing and able to provide resources and support. This theory implies that a female will seek quality in her mate, so from the evolutionary perspective women should be attracted to males who have social and economic advantages and who appear willing to share these resources.

On the other hand, a male's reproductive capacity is only limited by the number of females who are willing to reproduce with him, thus males may be more inclined to seek many fertile mates. Also, males will want to make sure they are not tricked into raising the offspring of another male.

Both males and females will be interested in good genetic quality in order that their offspring survive. Buss proposed that 'baby' features evoke attraction and caregiving, that humans have evolved a preference for these facial characteristics to ensure we care for our young and that men all over the world share the same ideal of beauty.

Research evidence: Waynforth and Dunbar (1995)

Waynforth and Dunbar (1995) analysed personal adverts in US newspapers. They found that compared to 25% of females, 42% of males wanted younger partners. Also 44% of males advertised for physically attractive partners but only 22% of females did. Females advertised their attractiveness but males advertised their economic resources.

Evaluation

Evolutionary explanations for mate choice are reductionist, and human behaviour is influenced by social, cultural and cognitive factors so may be very different from animal behaviour.

Read Item 1 and your textbook.

1 **a** **Complete these sentences by adding an explanation.**

    i From an evolutionary perspective females prefer attractive males because...

....

....

    ii From an evolutionary perspective females prefer wealthy males because...

....

....

    iii From an evolutionary perspective females prefer generous males because...

....

....

  b **Summarise the evolutionary explanation to suggest why males and females look for different qualities in romantic partners.**

....

....

....

....

....

  c **Explain why evolutionary theory suggests males will look for more than one mate while females will look for quality in one mate.**

....

....

....

....

....

....

Item 2 Factors affecting attraction in romantic relationships

Self-disclosure

Self-disclosure comprises everything an individual chooses to tell the other person about himself or herself. There are two dimensions to self-disclosure — **breadth and depth** — and both are important in developing a relationship. It is easier for breadth to be expanded first in a relationship because it consists of outer layers of personality and everyday lives, such as occupations and preferences. Depth in disclosure is more difficult because it may include traits that we prefer to hide.

Intimacy in relationships cannot be achieved without self-disclosure. Most self-disclosure occurs early in the development of a relationship, but more intimate self-disclosure occurs later.

Self disclosure in marriage

Self-disclosure is a method of relationship maintenance. Partners learn a shared communication system, and disclosures are a large part of building that system. Research suggests that wives' perceptions of their husbands' self-disclosures are a strong predictor of how long a couple will stay together. Those who think their husbands are not sharing enough are likely to break up sooner.

Physical attractiveness

Physical attractiveness may be one of the most important factors in interpersonal attraction because, from an evolutionary perspective, physical characteristics, such as good skin and glossy hair, indicate breeding success. If a person is physically attractive we attribute other positive characteristics to them. This is called the **halo effect** and in the early stages of relationship formation physical attractiveness is an important factor.

Research evidence: is physical attractiveness an advantage?

Stewart, J. E. (1985) looked for a correlation between the attractiveness of defendants and the severity of punishment awarded. Sixty criminal trials were studied: 56 male and 4 female defendants were observed by at least two observers and rated on physical attractiveness, neatness, cleanliness and quality of dress which were combined to produce an attractiveness index. Stewart found that defendants who were judged to be less attractive received more severe punishment.

Research evidence: is physical attraction associated with positive characteristics?

Wheeler and Kim (1997) investigated the halo effect and found that American, Canadian and Korean students rated physically attractive people as more friendly, extrovert, happy and sociable. Landy and Siegall (1974) found that male participants rated essays (good and poor) as better if they were thought to be written by an attractive female.

Research evidence: the matching hypothesis

Walster et al. (1966) suggested that we are attracted to people whom we perceive to be similarly attractive to ourselves to avoid being rejected by potential partners who are more attractive than ourselves.

Walster, Aronson, Abrams and Rottman (1966) invited 664 students to attend a 'computer' dance. They were told they would be 'matched' to a partner by a computer.

Before the dance, each student completed a series of questionnaires, supposedly so that the computer could complete the 'matching'. In reality the students, who had been rated for physical attractiveness by the experimenters, were randomly allocated to pairs in which the only control was that the male was taller than the female. After the dance the students were asked to complete questionnaires on which they rated how much they liked their partner, whether they wanted to see their partner again, how attractive they found their partner and how attractive they thought their partner found them. The experiment found that in cases where the males and females were considered to be well matched in terms of attractiveness, they liked each other more and rated each other as more attractive.

Evaluation

Attractiveness may only be important in the early stages of a relationship. Murstein and Christie (1976) found a correlation between husbands' ratings of how satisfied they were with their marriage and how attractive they thought their wife was and thought them to be. They found no correlation between the wives' satisfaction with their marriage and their perception of their husbands' attractiveness or how attractive their husbands found them.

Filter theory

Kerckoff and Davis (1962) propose that **three filters** are important before we enter a relationship and at different times in a relationship. We start with a field of those who are available for relationships and gradually narrow them down to a sample of those whom we would consider as desirable partners.

- The first filter stage is the **social and demographic variables**, where we tend to pick people with similar educational and economic background to us.
- The second filter stage is the **similarity of attitudes and values**, where people with different values, attitudes and interests to us are filtered out.
- The third filter stage is the **complementarity of emotional needs**, where we decide how well as two people we will fit together as a couple.

Evaluation

The filter model highlights the importance of demographic factors and similarity of attitudes and values in relationships, but the theory was written in 1962 which means that there is low historical validity (a temporal bias) as the research was conducted at a time when Western ideals were dominant and much research into filter theory is based on biased samples of students.

Read Item 2 and your textbook.

2 a Explain what is meant by self-disclosure.

....

....

....

b What is the difference between breadth of self-disclosure and depth of self-disclosure?

....

....

....

c What is meant by the 'halo effect'?

....

....

....

d A psychologist was interested in finding out how people chose their partners, so she interviewed 20 male and 20 female students and asked them what first attracted them to their partner. Explain how social desirability bias may influence this research.

....

....

....

....

e Explain what is meant by the matching hypothesis.

....

....

....

f In the Walster et al. computer dance study how is the sample biased?

....

....

....

....

g **Suggest why the Walster 'computer dance' study gives a reductionist explanation for interpersonal attraction.**

h **How might filter theory explain why a significant number of people meet their eventual partners at work?**

Item 3 Theories of romantic relationships

Social exchange theory: Thibaut and Kelley (1959)

Social exchange theory assumes that relationships are based on 'exchanges' in which each person seeks to maximise their rewards and minimise their costs and thus make a profit. The theory proposes that people stay in relationships when they are 'in profit' but that relationships may fail when either partner's costs exceed their rewards.

This theory proposes **four stages** in the development of a relationship:

- **Stage 1: sampling stage** in which the potential costs and rewards of a new relationship are considered and compared to other known relationships.
- **Stage 2: bargaining stage** in which partners receive and give rewards to test whether a deeper relationship is worthwhile.
- **Stage 3: commitment stage** in which relationship predictability increases and, because each partner knows how to 'get rewards' from the other, costs are reduced.
- **Stage 4: institutionalisation stage** in which norms are developed and patterns of rewards and costs established for each partner.

The theory proposes a **comparison level** by which people judge all their relationships. Our personal comparison level is the accumulation of all our relationship experiences and if we judge that the profit from a potential new relationship is greater than our comparison level then the partner will be viewed positively and a new relationship be formed. If we judge that the profit from a potential new relationship is less than our comparison level then the partner will be viewed negatively and no new relationship formed.

Research evidence: relationships based on profit and loss?

Rusbalt and Martz (1995) propose that women stay in abusive relationships because their investment is high (children and somewhere to live) but the cost of leaving is higher (nowhere to live and no money). Thus the woman is still 'in relationship profit' and she will remain in the relationship.

Evaluation

The theory proposes that the basis for the formation of human relationships is self-interest so perhaps the model only explains the formation of relationships in individualistic cultures. Also the theory is based on subjective judgement of what constitutes a reward, cost or profit, and thus can be used to justify almost any behaviour in terms of a calculated profit outcome.

15

Equity theory

The **equity theory** of relationships assumes that people try to ensure that their relationships are fair. This theory predicts that partners should feel equally dissatisfied if they under or over benefit and the greater the dissatisfaction the less likely it is that the relationship will continue.

The theory proposes that an equitable relationship is one in which one partner's benefits divided by their costs is equal to the other partner's benefits divided by their costs. If the result of this calculation results in perceived inequity (unfairness) we may try to restore fairness in one or more of the following ways:

- change the amount we put into or receive from the relationship
- change our evaluation of relative inputs and outputs to restore the appearance of equity
- be persuaded by the partner that our perception of relative inputs and outputs is wrong

Research evidence: Hatfield et al. (1979)

Hatfield et al. (1979) asked newly married couples about equity in their relationships. They found that underbenefited partners were the least satisfied, over-benefited the next and those who perceived their relationship to be equitable to be most satisfied.

Evaluation

Equity theory takes a 'rational economist' approach to explaining human relationships, but in relationships people are influenced by emotion rather than by rational thought. Perhaps such explanations only apply to short-term relationships in young people in Western culture. Also it is difficult to gain a valid measure of a person's subjective assessment of their inputs to, and benefits from, their relationships as their judgement of these may vary from day to day.

The investment model

Commitment is an important factor in maintaining relationships. Rusbult (1980) defined commitment as 'a person's intention to maintain the relationship and to remain psychologically attached to it'. Rusbult's **investment model of commitment** consists of three processes that are positively associated with commitment:

- **Satisfaction level** refers to the positive versus negative emotions experienced in a relationship. A person whose needs are met by his or her partner will enjoy a higher level of satisfaction.
- The **quality of alternatives** is defined as the attractiveness of the best obtainable alternative to a relationship.

- **Investment size** is how much an individual has already invested in the relationship. A person may stay in a relationship because they have already invested significantly in it.

Rusbult proposes that two other factors are linked to commitment:

- **Equity.** Rusbult suggests that fairness in a relationship is important because unfairness causes distress, and a partner in an inequitable relationship will be less committed to the relationship and may want to end the relationship.
- **Social support** such as family and friends. If family and friends approve of and support the relationship this produces a positive influence on commitment causing the couple to stay together longer.

Research evidence: Sprecher (1988)

Sprecher (1988) studied the extent to which different factors explain commitment to relationships. Data were collected from 197 couples. Relationship commitment was predicted to correlate positively with satisfaction, investment and social support, and correlate negatively with alternative quality and inequity. Results showed that the variables except investment were related (as predicted) to relationship commitment.

Evaluation

Qualitative factors, such as satisfaction with a relationship, may vary from week to week so it is difficult to gain a reliable measure of a person's subjective assessment of their investment in a relationship. Also much research into relationships is based on self-report of student samples, and the relationships of young people are usually more volatile than the relationships of older people.

The breakdown of relationships

Duck (1999) proposed three factors to explain why relationships break down:

- **Lack of social skills.** Some people lack social and interpersonal skills which leads others to perceive them as uninteresting and disinterested in 'relating to them'.
- **Lack of stimulation.** According to social exchange theory, lack of stimulation leads to boredom and to the end of the relationship.
- **Maintenance difficulties.** If partners are separated so that daily contact is decreased it may be difficult for the relationship to survive.

The four-stage model of relationship breakdown (Duck 1999)

- **Stage 1: intrapsychic phase.** With little outward show of dissatisfaction one partner may be inwardly re-evaluating the relationship in terms of the costs and benefits.
- **Stage 2: the dyadic phase.** The dissatisfied person tells the other partner. There may be arguments as to who is responsible but both partners are aware that the relationship may end.
- **Stage 3: the social phase.** Partners have informed friends and family about the problems in the relationship. Friends and family may speed up the eventual ending of the relationship, perhaps by interfering, and may also provide social support when the relationship ends.
- **Stage 4: the grave dressing phase.** Both partners try to justify leaving the relationship and construct a representation of the failed relationship that does not present them in unfavourable terms.

Evaluation

The Duck model shows the processes that take place when a relationship fails. Relationship counsellors can use this model to help repair failing relationships. However, the model does not explain why relationships break down.

Read Item 3 and your textbook.

3 a   Complete these sentences by adding an explanation.

   i   Social exchange theory is a cognitive explanation of relationships because...

....

....

   ii   Equity theory is a cognitive explanation of relationships because...

....

....

   iii   The investment model of relationships is based on self-reported evidence because...

....

....

  b   Milo lives in Paris and his partner Milandra lives in London. Why, according to Duck, may their relationship break down?

....

....

....

  c   Outline the four stages in the development of a relationship proposed by social exchange theory.

....

....

....

....

....

....

....

d Suggest one reason why it may be difficult to obtain a valid measure of the costs and benefits of a relationship.

....

....

....

....

e Emic constructs are traits that are specific to a certain culture. Suggest why the equity theory of relationships may be an emic construct.

....

....

....

....

....

....

....

f List one of the limitations of social exchange theory.

....

....

....

....

g Summarise Rusbult's investment model of commitment to a relationship.

....

....

....

....

....

....

h List one similarity between the social exchange theory and equity theory of relationships.

....

....

....

....

....

....

i   Summarise the four stages of relationship breakdown as suggested by Duck (1999).

j   What is the difference between the intrapsychic phase and the dyadic phase of relationship breakdown?

Item 4 Virtual relationships in social media

Virtual relationships

Electronically mediated interaction changes the way in which relationships develop and are maintained. Physical attraction and eye contact is absent and what is written (the text) increases in importance. Electronically mediated communication offers potential partners reduced information to go on when developing a relationship.

This reduction in cues leads to a form of deindividuation in which partners who are more or less anonymous may behave in an uninhibited manner and/or may breach social norms.

Advantages and disadvantages of virtual relationships

Electronic relationships have advantages. Duck (1999) reports that those who lack social skills, who live in rural areas, or who have physical handicaps may benefit. Internet chat rooms allow people to make a range of friends they would otherwise not get the opportunity to meet in 'real life'.

Young (1999) proposes the Social Identity model of Deindividuation (SIDE) and suggests that in computer-mediated communication awareness of individual identity is replaced by awareness of group identity and that being anonymous leads to strong social relationships in groups that meet on the internet.

Perhaps the main disadvantage of electronic relationships is the possibility of deception. Van Gelder (1985) describes a case in which a male psychiatrist pretended to be 'Joan' who had supposedly been injured in a road accident. 'Joan' set up an online support group for other disabled women and over 2 years deceived many women by forming intense friendships and romances.

Virtual relationships: self-disclosure

The development of a virtual relationship is related to an increase in self-disclosure. Being able to disclose the characteristics of one's true self can create bonds of understanding between people and heighten intimacy in a virtual relationship.

The ability to be **anonymous** in a virtual relationship is important because, when anonymous, the costs and risks of social sanctions are reduced. In a face-to-face relationship there is often a cost to disclosing negative aspects of one's self. These barriers are usually not present in virtual relationships and research suggests that in virtual relationships people often reveal themselves more intimately than they do in face-to-face relationships.

Virtual relationships: the absence of gating

Gating features are the physical or material barriers that may arise between people when they interact in person. Physical appearance, age, clothing, race and class distinctions all function as distractions to the expression of one's true self. In virtual relationships, such gating features do not exist and when you talk to someone online you are able to be your true self without the usual physical gating features present in face-to-face encounters.

Item 5 Parasocial relationships

Parasocial relationships are one-sided relationships, where one person extends emotional energy, interest and time, and the other party, the persona, is completely unaware of the other's existence. For some, the one-sided nature of the relationship is a relief from strained relationships in their real life. Reality television and social media allow viewers to share the personal lives of television personas and celebrities who openly share their opinions and activities through outlets such as Twitter and Facebook.

Advantages of parasocial relationships

- Parasocial relationships can help teach because people are more likely to listen to a 'virtual role model'.
- Parasocial relationships are advantageous because the person gains support from the relationship.
- Parasocial relationships can broaden one's social network.

Disadvantages of parasocial relationships

- Parasocial relationships may be pathological and a symptom of loneliness and social anxiety.
- People can be tricked into forming relationships with confidence tricksters and criminals.

Levels of parasocial relationships

Giles and Maltby said parasocial relationships can occur and progress in three levels:
- **Entertainment-social:** fans are attracted to celebrities because it provides entertainment.

- **Intense-personal:** fans feel a connection (real or imagined) with the celebrity.
- **Borderline pathological:** fans have uncontrollable fantasies about their celebrity which are completely unconnected to reality and which can lead to 'addicted' behaviours such as stalking and obsession.

The absorption-addiction model

McCutcheon et al. (2002) suggest that people seek parasocial relationships to fill the dissatisfaction they feel in their lives. The absorption-addiction model applies to individuals with a weak sense of identity and consists of two stages:
- **Stage 1: absorption.** The person's attention is entirely focused on the celebrity and they find out everything they can about him or her.
- **Stage 2: addiction.** The individual craves greater and greater closeness to the chosen celebrity and becomes increasingly delusional in thinking and behaviour.

This model argues that a personal life crisis may lead an individual to move from the absorption to the addiction stage and predicts a correlation between poor psychological health and the strength of parasocial relationships. Maltby et al. (2004) suggested that intense celebrity worship was associated with poorer mental health, and with depression, social dysfunction and low life satisfaction.

Attachment theory

Keinlen (1998) and McCann (2001) suggest that parasocial relationships are formed by people who are 'insecurely attached' because parasocial relationships do not come with the threat of disappointment and breakup.

The attachment theory of parasocial relationships is a psychodynamic explanation as it argues that the tendency to form parasocial relationships originates in the early childhood relationships between the child and the primary caregiver. This theory argues that those with insecure attachments are more likely to become strongly attached to celebrities. Leets (1999) studied 115 students and found that attachment styles are related to parasocial behaviour. Those with anxious-ambivalent attachment styles were the most likely to form parasocial relationships.

Read Items 4 and 5 and your textbook.

4 **a** **Suggest one reason why individuals might form virtual relationships with those they would not consider to be potential partners in 'real life'.**

....

....

....

....

....

....

....

b **List two differences between 'normal relationships' and virtual relationships.**

....

....

....

....

....

....

....

c **Explain what is meant by 'the absence of gating in virtual relationships'.**

....

....

....

....

....

....

....

d In a parasocial relationship what is the difference between the absorption stage and the addiction stage?

....

....

....

....

....

....

e Explain how attachment styles may predict the formation of parasocial relationships.

....

....

....

....

....

....

....

....

....

....

....

Exam-style questions

5 a Which one of the following sequences, A, B, C or D, shows the correct order of Duck's phases of relationship breakdown?   1 mark

Circle the letter of the answer that you think is correct.

A Dyadic, intrapsychic, social, grave dressing

B Intrapsychic, dyadic, social, grave dressing

C Intrapsychic, social, dyadic, grave dressing

D Social, dyadic, intrapsychic, grave dressing

b Which of A, B, C or D is NOT a feature of the investment model of relationships?   1 mark

Circle the letter of the answer that you think is correct.

A Investment

B Satisfaction

C Shared friends

D Commitment

c   One theory of relationship formation is known as filter theory. Three stages of filter
    are proposed. The first filter stage is the social and demographic variables where we
    tend to pick people with similar educational and economic background to us.
    Outline the second filter stage.   **1 mark**

d   Social exchange theory assumes that relationships are based on 'exchanges' in which
    each person seeks to maximise their rewards and minimise their costs. Outline any
    two of the four stages in the development of a relationship.   **2 marks**

e   Psychologists suggest that relationships that start over the internet are more
    intimate than those which start in a face-to-face physical communication
    because you are able to be your true self without the physical gating features
    present in face-to-face encounters.

    List three features that may act as gating features in face-to-face relationships.   **3 marks**

f   From the evolutionary perspective, explain why physical attractiveness may be
    an important factor in interpersonal attraction.   **4 marks**

g Discuss the extent to which psychologists can explain the breakdown of relationships.

16 marks

Topic 3

Stress

Item 1 The physiology of stress

The general adaptation syndrome (GAS)

Selye (1956) proposed that stress leads to a depletion of the body's resources, leaving the animal vulnerable to illness. He proposed that the body reacts in the same way to all stressors and he called this the 'general adaptation syndrome' (GAS). There are three stages in the GAS model:

- **Stage 1: alarm.** When we perceive a stressor, the autonomic nervous system (ANS) responds. Adrenaline, noradrenaline and corticosteroids (stress hormones) are released into the bloodstream. The physiological reaction is increased arousal levels (i.e. increased heart rate raised, blood pressure and tensed muscles) in readiness for a physical 'fight-or-flight' response.
- **Stage 2: resistance.** If the stressor continues, the bodily reaction (the fight-or-flight response) ceases, but output from the adrenal cortex continues and the adrenal glands may become enlarged.
- **Stage 3: exhaustion.** If the stressor continues for a long time, the body's resources are reduced and alarm signs, such as increased blood pressure, may return. The immune system may be damaged and stress-related diseases such as high blood pressure and cardiovascular disorders are more likely to occur.

The hypothalamic-pituitary-adrenal system (HPA)

The stress response originates in the hypothalamus and includes the pituitary and adrenal glands. This HPA axis is responsible for arousing the ANS in response to a stressor. Under stress, the sympathetic branch of the nervous system stimulates the adrenal gland to release adrenaline, noradrenaline and corticosteroids into the bloodstream. This produces the physiological reactions, such as increased heart rate and blood pressure and a dry mouth, known as the 'fight-or-flight' response.

Sympathomedullary pathway (SAM)

The SAM is activated by an acute stressor. In acute stress the hypothalamus activates the adrenal medulla. The adrenal medulla is the part of the ANS that secretes the hormone adrenaline and adrenaline prepares the body for a **fight-or-flight response**.

The physiological reaction to increased adrenalin includes increased heart rate, the arousal of the sympathetic nervous system and changes in the body such as decreases in digestion and increases in sweating, pulse rate and blood pressure.

The stress hormone cortisol

The stress hormone cortisol can cause damage to health because raised cortisol levels reduce immune function and increase the risk of depression and mental illness. Cortisol is released in response to stress by the adrenal glands as part of the fight-or-flight mechanism.

Selye defined two types of stress — eustress (good stress) and distress (bad stress). During distress when cortisol is released your body becomes mobilised and ready for 'fight-or-flight' and unless there is some physical action (e.g. you run away from the snarling dog) cortisol levels build up in the blood which presents risk to health. In comparison, during eustress there is a heightened state of arousal and cortisol levels return to normal on completion of the task.

Read Item 1 and your textbook.

1 a When talking about stress, what does the acronym GAS stand for?

....

b Fill in the blank spaces in the following sentences.

  i The hypothalamic-pituitary-adrenal axis is responsible for arousing the

  _____ in response to a stressor.

  ii An acute stressor activates the _____ .

c What happens in GAS stage 1 — the alarm stage?

....

....

....

....

d Outline the effects of the stress hormone cortisol.

....

....

....

....

e When we are in a stressful situation what causes the 'flight-or-fight' response symptoms such as increased heart rate and blood pressure and a dry mouth?

....

....

....

....

....

f Outline how stress affects the immune system.

....

....

....

....

....

....

Item 2 The role of stress in illness

Stress and the immune system

The immune system defends the body against bacteria, viruses and cancerous cells. When we are stressed, the ability of the immune system to protect us is reduced, leading to an increased likelihood of physical illness. This weakening of the immune system is called the **immunosuppressive effect of stress**. In long-term stress, such as stage 3 of Selye's GAS, increased levels of corticosteroids reduce the production of antibodies (a direct effect).

Research evidence: Kiecolt-Glaser et al. (1984)

Kiecolt-Glaser et al. (1984) looked for evidence of a difference in immune response in high- and low-stress conditions, and to see whether factors such as anxiety were associated with immune system functioning. Seventy-five first-year medical students gave blood samples 1 month before their final exams, and again after they had sat two papers on the first day of the exams. In comparison with the first blood sample, natural killer cell activity was significantly reduced in the second sample. It was most reduced in those students who were experiencing other stressful events, and in those who reported feeling anxious and depressed. This suggests that stress can be associated with reduced immune system function. However, it is not possible to say how long-lasting the reduced effectiveness of the immune system might be.

Stress and cardiovascular disorders

Cardiovascular disorders are disorders of the heart and blood vessels and are sometimes linked with stress. People who experience stress may engage in unhealthy activities, such as smoking and drinking alcohol, in an attempt to relieve the stress and so stress may be an **indirect cause** of illness because these behaviours increase the likelihood that the person may develop a cardiovascular disorder.

Long-term stress may also have a direct effect on the cardiovascular system. Stress causes increased heart rate and raised blood pressure and can damage blood vessels because adrenaline and noradrenaline contribute to increases in blood cholesterol levels, leading to blockages in blood vessels, causing strokes or heart attacks.

Read Item 2 and your textbook.

2 **a** **What do psychologists mean when they say stress has an indirect effect on health?**

....

....

....

....

b **Explain why long-term stress may cause physical illness.**

....

....

....

....

c **Suggest why it is difficult to prove conclusively that long-term stress causes physical illness.**

....

....

....

....

Item 3 Sources of stress

Major sources of stress include:

- **Life events.** Events that cause us to change the way we live, such as marriage, and adjusting to these changes, may cause stress.
- **Daily hassles.** The regular hassles of everyday life such as being stuck in a traffic jam also cause stress.
- **The workplace.** The kind of work people do, where they work and with whom they work, can be a source of stress.

Life changes and the Social Readjustment Rating Scale (SRRS)

Holmes and Rahe (1967) constructed an instrument for measuring stress. They found that the cumulative amount of life change is related to psychological and physiological illness. They compiled a questionnaire called the Social Readjustment Rating Scale (SRRS) listing 43 types of life event that require readjustment, for example, marriage, death of a spouse, change of job.

People complete the SRRS by ticking the life events they have experienced in the last 12 months. Holmes and Rahe found that people with high life change scores on the SRRS were likely to experience some physical illness and a person having 300 points over 12 months had an 80% chance of becoming ill. According to Holmes and Rahe, stress can be objectively measured by the SRRS and stressful life changes cause physical illness.

Evaluation

How each person experiences a life event is different and life events other than the 43 on the SRRS may also cause stress. Also, most of the 43 life events listed on the SRRS are only likely to be experienced by mature adults with families and are infrequent. The daily small hassles of life may be a more significant cause of stress.

Daily hassles and stress

DeLongis et al. (1982) created the hassles scale which measures positive events (uplifts) as well as hassles. They found that the hassles scale was a better predictor of ill health (in people over 45) than life changes. The frequency and intensity of daily hassles significantly correlated to ill health.

Kanner et al. (1981) found that the hassles scale was a better predictor of psychological and physiological symptoms than the life events scores. Hassles and symptoms of stress were significantly correlated, and uplifts were positively related to reduced symptoms for women but not for men.

Stress in the workplace

Stress in the workplace can originate in six areas:

(1) **Interpersonal factors.** Good relationships with co-workers can reduce stress in the workplace.
(2) **Workload and pressure.** Having too much work to do and strict deadlines can cause stress.
(3) **The physical environment.** This may be noisy or too hot or too cold, or may involve unsociable hours, such as working night shifts.
(4) **Role stress.** Worry about job security or responsibility may cause stress.
(5) **Role conflict.** Having to express one emotion while feeling another may cause stress.
(6) **Control.** How much control people have may be a factor in how stressful a job is perceived to be.

Research evidence: factors that may cause stress in the workplace

Margolis and Kroes (1974) investigated role conflict. They found that when a job requires workers to express one emotion, e.g. being calm and cheerful, while really feeling another emotion, e.g. being unhappy or worried, this causes role conflict. Nurses, teachers and paramedics are likely to suffer stress caused by role conflict.

Marmot et al. (1997) investigated whether perceived control is an important factor in work-related stress. In their study of 7,000 civil service employees who worked in London, participants who were less senior and who felt they had less control and less social support were more likely to have cardiovascular disorders. It was concluded that how much control people have at work, and how much social support people receive from colleagues, may be factors in whether they suffer from stress-related illness.

Read Item 3 and your textbook.

3 a Give one example of a life-changing event.

....

b Outline the difference between a life-changing event and a daily hassle.

....

....

....

....

c How does the SRRS measure the amount of life changes an individual has experienced?

....

....

....

....

....

d Identify a sample of the population for which the SRRS may not be an appropriate way to measure stress and explain why.

....

....

....

....

e Susie works on a checkout in a busy supermarket where there is almost always a queue of customers waiting. What factors related to her job may cause Susie to feel stressed?

....

....

....

....

....

f How are workload and lack of control causes of stress-related ill health?

....

....

....

....

....

....

Item 4 Measuring stress

Using self-report scales to measure stress

Holmes and Rahe (1967): Social Readjustment Rating Scale (SRRS)

They defined stress as the amount of life changes people had experienced during a fixed period and constructed the SRRS to measure stress. When completing the SRRS people tick the life events they have experienced in the last 12 months, thus giving a quantitative measure of the amount of life change (stress). Using the SRRS stress can be objectively measured as a life changes score. High scores on the SRRS (high-stress scores) predict physical illness.

Kanner et al. (1981): daily hassles and uplifts scale

A 117 item hassles scale and a 135 uplifts scale were developed to examine the relationship between hassles and health. A longitudinal study with repeated measures design was used and participants filled out the life events scale as well as the hassles and uplifts scale. The hassles scale was a better predictor of psychological and physiological symptoms than were the life events scores.

Evaluation

Self-report scales may lack validity — as people's feelings of stress will vary from day to day and people may over or under estimate the degree to which they are experiencing stress.

Using physiological measures of stress

Research evidence: skin conductance response

Skin conductance response, also known as galvanic skin response (GSR), is a method of measuring the electrical conductance of the skin, which varies depending on the amount of sweat-induced moisture on the skin. Sweat is controlled by the sympathetic nervous system, so skin conductance is used as an indication of psychological or physiological arousal. If the sympathetic branch of the autonomic nervous system is highly aroused, then sweat gland activity also increases, which in turn increases skin conductance. In this way, skin conductance can be used as a measure of emotional and sympathetic responses.

Geer and Maisel (1972) investigated the effect of control in reducing stress. In a laboratory experiment 60 student participants were shown photographs of dead car crash victims and their stress levels were measured by GSR and heart rate through ECG monitoring. Participants were randomly assigned to three conditions:

- Group 1: were given control over how long they looked at the images for.
- Group 2: the group had no control but did know what was happening.
- Group 3: were not given any control.

Group 1 who could control how long they saw the image for experienced the least stress, Group 2, who knew what was coming but did not have any control experienced higher stress, and Group 3 who had no control showed the highest stress levels.

Research evidence: stress hormones in urine

Johansson et al. (1978) investigated whether work stressors increase stress-related physiological arousal and illness. Participants were a high-risk group of 14 'finishers' in a Swedish sawmill whose work was machine-paced and repetitive, and whose productivity determined the wage rates for the entire factory. These 'finishers' were compared with a low-risk group of 10 cleaners, whose work was more varied and self-paced. Levels of stress-related hormones (adrenaline and noradrenaline) in the urine were measured on work days and rest days. Records were kept of stress-related illness and absenteeism.

The high-risk group of 14 finishers secreted more stress hormones (adrenaline and noradrenaline) on work days than on rest days, and higher levels than the control group. The high-risk group of finishers also showed significantly higher levels of stress-related illness and higher levels of absenteeism than the low-risk group of cleaners.

Johansson concluded that a combination of work stressors, especially repetitive machine-paced work and high levels of responsibility, lead to long-term physiological arousal which leads to stress-related illness and absenteeism.

Evaluation

Physiological measurements give scientific and objective data that can be used to make comparisons such as before and after stress treatment, but physiological measurements of stress reduce the psychological and subjective experience of stress to simplistic single factor biological measurements.

Read Item 4 and your textbook.

4   a   **Suggest one advantage of using self-report to measure stress.**

....

....

....

    b   **Suggest one disadvantage of using self-report to measure stress.**

....

....

....

    c   **Explain why measuring the amount of cortisol in saliva is a reductionist measurement of stress.**

....

....

....

....

....

    d   **When measuring stress, suggest how researchers could increase validity.**

....

....

....

....

....

Item 5 Individual differences in stress

Personality factors may be involved in how people respond to stressors.

Type A and B personality

Friedman and Rosenman (1974) defined two types of behaviour pattern, Type A and Type B, and studied their relation to coronary heart disease (CHD).

Type A behaviour: Type A people move, eat and talk rapidly, are competitive and tend to judge themselves by the number of successes they have rather than the quality of their successes. Type A individuals are hard-driving, impatient and aggressive and tend to be achievement-oriented.

Type B behaviour: Type B people seldom feel any sense of time urgency or impatience, are not preoccupied with their achievements and seldom become angry or irritable, tend to enjoy their recreation, and are free of guilt about relaxing.

Friedman and Rosenman (1974) studied 3,000 men aged between 39 and 59, who were healthy at the start of the study; 8½ years later, 257 of the men in the sample were diagnosed as having CHD — 70% of those with CHD had been classified as Type A. The Type A men were also found to have higher levels of adrenaline and cholesterol. Twice as many Type A men had died compared with Type Bs. Type As also had higher blood pressure, higher cholesterol and other symptoms of CHD.

Type C personality

Type C people think analytically and tend to be problem solvers because they focus on details. The Type C personality has difficulty expressing emotion, particularly negative emotions such as anger and people with type C personality traits may display pathological niceness and conflict avoidance and compliance. Temoshock (1987) suggested that Type C personalities are 'cancer prone' because they respond to stress with a sense of helplessness.

The hardy personality

Kobasa (1979) proposed that some people are better able to deal with stress (the hardy personality) and that all people could learn to behave in this way in order to cope better. The key traits of a hardy personality, known as the three Cs, are having:

- a strong sense of personal **control**
- a strong sense of purpose or **commitment**
- the ability to see problems positively, as **challenges** to be overcome rather than as stressors

According to Kobasa, hardy individuals are committed to face problems and will not stop until they find resolutions. They view change as a challenge to be overcome.

Kobasa researched the link between a hardy personality and stress levels. The stress levels of 800 business executives were measured using Holmes and Rahe's SRRS. Hardiness was also assessed using a 'hardiness' test — 150 of the executives had high levels of stress and those with low levels of illness were more likely to have scored high on the Hardy personality test.

Evaluation of individual differences in stress

Using psychometric tests to measure personality may raise issues of validity and reliability. Also the link between stress levels and personality types is correlational and thus cannot be said to be causational.

Item 6 Managing and coping with stress

Physiological treatments for stress focus on the reduction of the physical symptoms. Psychological approaches focus on encouraging people to deal with the causes of their stress.

Psychologists categorise coping strategies as physiological or psychological and/or emotion-focused or problem-focused:
- Emotion-focused strategies attempt to reduce the symptoms of anxiety by taking a physiological approach, for example anti-anxiety drugs may be used.
- Problem-focused strategies attempt to change how people respond to stressors, by using cognitive therapies or by encouraging people to increase their social support

Drug therapy

Drugs aim to reduce the physiological, or bodily, response to stress.

Benzodiazepine is an anti-anxiety (anxiolytic) drug and its brand names include Librium and Valium. These drugs slow down the activity of the central nervous system (CNS) and reduce anxiety by enhancing the activity of a natural biochemical substance, gamma-amino-butyric-acid (GABA). GABA is the body's natural form of anxiety relief. It also reduces serotonin activity.

Beta-blockers act on the sympathetic nervous system (SNS) rather than the brain. They reduce heart rate and blood pressure and thus reduce the harmful effects of stress.

Advantages

- Drugs quickly reduce the physiological effects of stress and people prefer drug therapies because 'taking a pill is easy'.
- Drugs do not require people to change the way they think or behave and can be used in conjunction with psychological methods.

Limitations

- All drugs have side effects.
- Long-term use of drugs can lead to physical and psychological dependency.
- Drugs treat the symptoms of stress but do not address the causes of the problem.

Biofeedback

Biofeedback works because our minds can influence the automatic functions of our bodies. Using a special machine, people can learn to control processes such as heart rate and blood pressure. Biofeedback machines provide information about the systems in the body that are affected by stress. There are four stages in learning biofeedback:

- The person is attached to a machine that monitors changes in heart rate and blood pressure and gives feedback.
- The person learns to control the symptoms of stress by deep breathing and muscle relaxation. This slows down their heart rate, making them feel more relaxed.
- The biofeedback from the machine acts like a reward and encourages the person to repeat the breathing techniques.
- Through practice, the person learns to repeat the breathing techniques in stressful situations.

Advantages

- There are no side effects.
- It reduces symptoms and gives people a sense of control.
- The learned techniques can be generalised to other stressful situations.

Limitations

- It requires specialist equipment and expert supervision.
- It requires the stressed person to commit time and effort.
- Anxious people may find learning biofeedback techniques difficult.

Stress inoculation therapy (Meichenbaum (1985)

Stress inoculation therapy (SIT) is a form of cognitive behavioural therapy (CBT). The aim of SIT is to train people to deal with stress before it becomes a problem.

Preparing people for stress can be like an inoculation to prevent a disease. Stress 'inoculation' proceeds in three stages.

- **Conceptualisation.** In this stage the client identifies and expresses their feelings and fears and is educated about stress. The client is encouraged to re-live stressful situations, analysing what was stressful about them and how they attempted to deal with them.
- **Skill acquisition and rehearsal.** In this stage the client is taught how to relax, how to think differently about stressors and how to express their emotions as well as specific skills such as time management.
- **Application and follow-through.** In this stage the trainer guides the client through progressively more threatening situations so that the patient can apply their newly acquired skills.

Increasing hardiness (Kobasa 1977)

The aim of increasing hardiness is to encourage people to respond to stressors in a positive manner, and to teach people the behavioural, physiological and cognitive skills that enable them to cope with stressors. Hardiness training involves three stages:

- **Focusing.** Patients are taught to recognise the signs of stress, such as muscle tension and tiredness, and to identify the sources of the stress.
- **Re-living stressful encounters.** Patients are asked to re-live stressful situations and to analyse these situations so that they can learn from past experience.
- **Self-improvement.** Patients use the insights gained to help them see stressors as challenges that can be coped with, leading to improved self-confidence and an enhanced sense of control.

Gender differences and stress

Gender may be an important factor in stress:
- Women are biologically more able to cope with stress.
- Women are socialised to cope better with stress.
- Women tend to drink and smoke less and may do less stressful work.

From an **evolutionary** (**biological**) **perspective**, men should respond to situations of danger with the 'fight-or-flight' arousal response, whereas women should respond by looking after young ones and each other. From a **social perspective**, males and females are socialised in different ways. Women learn to use social networks more and this may reduce their stress. When coping with stress, women tend to use more emotion-focused strategies than men who use problem-focused coping strategies.

Emotion-focused stress management

Lazarus and Folkman (1984) suggested there are two types of coping responses — emotion-focused and problem-focused.

- **Emotion-focused coping** involves trying to reduce the negative emotional responses associated with stress such as anxiety, depression and frustration. This may be the only realistic option when the source of stress is outside the person's control.
- **Emotion-focused strategies** include keeping busy to take your mind off the issue, letting off steam to other people, ignoring the problem in the hope that it will go away.

Problem-focused stress management

Problem-focused coping targets the causes of stress in practical ways which tackle the problem that is causing stress, consequently directly reducing the stress. Problem-focused strategies include:

- **Taking control** which involves changing the relationship between yourself and the source of stress, for example leaving a stressful job.
- **Information seeking** which is a cognitive response to stress as the individual tries to understand the situation and puts into place cognitive strategies to avoid it in future.
- **Evaluating the pros and cons** of different ways of dealing with the stressor.

Social support

Research suggests that social support helps in stressful situations because when people have others to turn to they are psychologically better able to handle stressors such as unemployment and the everyday problems of living. Researchers make a distinction between perceived and received support:

- **Perceived support** refers to a recipient's subjective judgment that he or she will be offered effective help during times of need.
- **Received support** refers to specific supportive actions offered during times of need.

Support can come from many sources, such as family, friends, pets, and neighbours.

Types of social support

There are four common types of social support:

- **Emotional support (esteem support)** is the offering of empathy, affection, love or caring. Providing emotional support can let the individual know that he or she is valued (esteem support).
- **Instrumental support** is the provision of financial assistance or services and this form of social support is the concrete ways people assist others.
- **Informational support** is the provision of advice or useful information to help someone solve a problem.
- **Companionship support** is the type of support that gives someone a sense of social belonging.

Research evdience

Wexler-Morrison et al. (1991) studied 133 women diagnosed as suffering from breast cancer and found that those who had a network of social support survived longer. The researchers suggested that social support may be effective because friends provide information and encouragement and also because 'sharing a problem' acts as a 'buffer' to guard against and reverse the effects of stress.

Evaluation of psychological approaches to stress management

Advantages

- Psychological approaches can be combined with other treatment methods to alleviate stress.
- Psychological approaches focus on the cause of stress and on ways of coping with it and are effective for both short- and long-term stressors.
- Psychological approaches lead to increased feelings of 'being in control' and so lead to increased self-confidence and self-efficacy.
- There are no physiological side effects.

Limitations

- Psychological approaches may only be successful with patients who are already determined to make the time and effort to help themselves.
- The research findings are based on biased samples of mainly white middle-class, well-educated people thus may not generalise to other populations.

Read Items 5–6 and your textbook.

5 a Briefly describe the personality characteristics of the Type A personality.

b Why is a Type B personality less likely to suffer stress-related illness?

c   Explain the difference between physiological and psychological methods of managing stress.

d   Explain how one drug treatment reduces the physiological symptoms of stress.

e   How did Kobasa define the hardy personality?

f   Suggest one advantage of using drugs to treat stress.

g Outline the processes involved when biofeedback is used to treat stress.

....
....
....
....
....
....
....
....
....

h Outline how stress inoculation therapy (SIT) can be used to help people manage stress.

....
....
....
....
....
....
....
....

i Ahmed has been made redundant is worried and stressed. Suggest two types of social support his friends could offer.

....
....
....
....
....
....

j Suggest why it may be difficult to gain a valid measure of how social support reduces stress.

....
....
....
....

k   Explain the difference between emotion-focused and problem-focused ways of coping with stress.

Exam-style questions

6 a   Kobasa (1979) found that some people deal with stress more effectively (the hardy personality). Outline the key traits of a hardy personality.
    `2 marks`

b   Explain the difference between instrumental social support and informational social support.
    `2 marks`

c Explain one disadvantage of using the Social Readjustment Rating Scale (SRRS) to measure stress. **2 marks**

d A factory makes frozen chicken products and other frozen and chilled food products. The factory employs 500 people and production is ongoing 24 hours a day, 7 days each week. There is a high level of sickness and absenteeism. Make one recommendation for change in the factory and explain why you think this change may reduce levels of sickness and absence. **4 marks**

e Discuss the extent to which stress can be said to cause physical illness. **8 marks** f Discuss psychological approaches to stress management.

8 marks

Topic 4

Aggression

Item 1 Neural and hormonal mechanisms in aggression

The limbic system

The limbic system is a set of evolutionarily primitive brain structures located on top of the brainstem and under the cortex. It is involved in aggression:

- Stimulation of the **amygdala** results in increased aggressive behaviour, while damage to this area reduces aggression.
- The **hypothalamus** has been shown to cause aggressive behaviour when electrically stimulated. It has receptors that help determine aggression levels based on their interactions with the neurotransmitters serotonin and vasopressin.

Serotonin and aggression

Serotonin is a neurotransmitter and **low levels of serotonin** appear to be linked with aggressive behaviour. The link between serotonin and aggression is tested through comparing levels of the serotonin metabolite 5-HIAA in participants' cerebrospinal fluid to a history of aggressive behaviour or actual aggression. If serotonin plays a key role in aggression, researchers would expect to see **reduced levels of 5-HIAA** in more aggressive people.

Research evidence

Stanley et al. (2000) compared the cerebrospinal fluid concentrations of 5-HIAA in aggressive and non-aggressive psychiatric patients. They found that aggressive participants had lower levels of 5-HIAA than the non-aggressive participants.

Testosterone and aggression

Testosterone is a male sex hormone (androgen) which influences aggressive behaviour. T models are proposed to explain how testosterone influences aggression:

- The **basal model of testosterone** proposes that testosterone causes a change in a person's dominance and that the more testosterone someone has, the more competitive and dominant they will become.

- The **reciprocal model of testosterone** proposes that testosterone levels are influenced by the level of dominance of an individual.

Research evidence

Mazur and Booth (1998) support the basal model of testosterone — they found that men with higher levels of testosterone were more likely to divorce and be involved in aggressive crime.

Dabbs (1987) investigated whether male criminals who had higher levels of testosterone had committed more violent crimes. A sample of 88 prison inmates, aged between 18 and 23, were rated on how tough they were by the guards and then they were split into four categories: 25 bo-hogs (tough inmates), 19 scrubs (weak inmates), 29 cell block (in-between) and 15 'cutters' (prisoners who self-harm). The bo-hogs' testosterone level average was significantly higher than the scrubs' testosterone level. Of the 11 inmates with the highest testosterone levels, 10 had committed violent crimes, but of the 11 inmates with the lowest testosterone levels, 9 had committed non-violent crimes. The researchers concluded that there was a positive relationship between testosterone levels and violent crime.

Evaluation

Serotonin and/or testosterone studies only show a correlation between neural and hormonal levels and aggression so it is not possible to say that serotonin or testosterone levels cause aggressive behaviour. Also, giving a biological cause for aggressive behaviour is reductionist and deterministic.

Genetic factors in aggression

Monoamine oxidase A, also known as **MAO-A**, is an enzyme that in humans is encoded by the MAO-A gene and that degrades amine neurotransmitters, such as dopamine, norepinephrine and serotonin. Mutation in the MAO-A gene results in monoamine oxidase deficiency. Monoamine oxidases (MAOs) are enzymes that are involved in the breakdown of neurotransmitters such as serotonin and dopamine and can influence the feelings and behaviour of individuals.

One version of the MAO-A gene has been referred to as the **warrior gene**. Research has shown that people with the low activity MAO-A gene showed higher levels of aggression than individuals with the high activity MAO-A gene and that low activity MAO-A could significantly predict aggressive behaviour in a high provocation situation.

Research evidence

Brunner (**1993**) identified Brunner syndrome which is a rare genetic disorder caused by a mutation in the MAO-A gene. It is characterised by lower than average IQ (typically about 85), problematic impulsive behaviour (such as arson and violence), as well as sleep disorders and mood swings. It was identified in 14 males from one family in 1993 and has since been discovered in additional families. Brunner syndrome is associated with a behavioural phenotype that includes disturbed regulation of impulsive aggression.

Evaluation

- Reductionist — giving a genetic explanation for aggressive behaviour ignores psychological evidence that suggests aggressive behaviour can be learned or has social causes.
- Biological determinism — giving a genetic explanation for aggressive behaviour suggests that people do not have free-will.
- Nature or nurture — genetic factors may increase the risk of aggression but only when combined with environmental factors.

Read Item 1 and your textbook.

1 a Fill in the blank spaces in the following sentences.

 i The _____ and the _____ are structures in the limbic system thought

   to be involved in aggressive behaviour.

 ii Low levels of the neurotransmitter _____ are thought to be associated with

   aggressive behaviour.

 iii High levels of the male sex hormone _____ may cause aggressive behaviour.

 b Why can we not be sure that the testosterone levels as measured in the Dabbs study were the same as the levels of testosterone in the men when they committed their crimes?

 ....

 ....

 ....

 ....

 ....

 ....

 c What does MAO-A stand for and what is it?

 ....

 ....

 ....

 ....

 ....

d What is the 'warrior gene'?

....

....

....

....

....

....

....

e Explain one limitation of suggesting that genes cause aggressive behaviour.

....

....

....

....

....

....

....

....

....

Item 2 Ethological and evolutionary explanations for aggression

Ethological explanation

Ethologists are interested in how animal behaviours increase an animal's chance of survival and reproduction. Lorenz proposed that aggression evolved in all animals (including humans) because it is adaptive, because the most aggressive animals control access to resources such as mates, food and territory. Lorenz proposed that certain environmental signals (e.g. the sight of a rival male) act as releasers of behaviour and that much animal behaviour is:

- instinctive and occurring in every member of the same species
- species specific and stereotyped
- not learned

For ethologists, instinct means a series of predictable behaviours in **fixed action patterns**. Such fixed action pattern behaviours are only enacted when a precise signal known as an **innate releasing mechanism** (IRM) is present. An example of an IRM is the gaping-beak movement performed by newly hatched chicks which stimulates the parent bird to feed them. An IRM is an external 'sign', but fixed action pattern behaviour may also require internal stimulation, for example hunger or the sex drive during mating.

Fixed action patterns

Lea (1984) described six characteristics of fixed action patterns.
(1) Stereotyped — the behaviour always occurs in the same form.
(2) Universal — the behaviour is found throughout the species.
(3) Independence of experience — the behaviour is not learned.
(4) Ballistic — once it starts the behaviour cannot be stopped.

(5) Singleness of purpose — the behaviour is used in one context only.

(6) Triggering stimuli — the behaviour is triggered by specific stimuli.

Some psychologists suggest there are innate releasing mechanisms in humans, for example:

- reflex behaviours like sucking
- babies smiling — elicit play from mother
- babies crying — elicit care from mother

Evaluation

If human behaviour was made of fixed action patterns it would be rigid and inefficient, reducing the probability of survival. Also, there are so many different types of human aggression that it is difficult to argue that human aggression is fixed action pattern behaviour.

Evolution of human aggression

Evolutionary psychologists argue that reproductive challenges explain aggressive behaviour. For example, without a DNA test, a man can never be certain that he is the biological father of his children which might explain why male sexual jealousy is often cited as a cause of aggression and domestic violence.

Aggression: infidelity and jealousy

Daly and Wilson (1988) propose that men have evolved different strategies to deter their partners from committing adultery, ranging from vigilance (e.g. watching their every move) to violence, and that these strategies are the result of male jealousy and paternal uncertainty. If a man's female partner is unfaithful and has a relationship with another man, he runs the risk of cuckoldry — he may unwittingly invest resources in rearing children that are not his own. Male sexual jealousy may therefore have evolved to prevent infidelity by women and reduce the risk of cuckoldry.

Shackleton et al. (2005) surveyed 461 men and 560 women who were all in heterosexual relationships. The men answered questions about their use of mate retention techniques, and the women were asked about their partners' use of mate retention techniques and how violent their male partners were. There was a positive correlation between men who used mate retention techniques of direct guarding and their use of violence. There was also a positive correlation (in women) between those who had jealous partners and being the victims of violence.

Evaluation

- **Application:** research into mate retention techniques is useful because educating people in these danger signs can reduce the likelihood of women becoming victims of violence.
- **Methodological issues:** surveys are a self-report method and therefore may not collect valid data about sensitive subjects such as aggression.
- **Gender bias:** research into domestic violence and infidelity is gender biased as the evolutionary argument for infidelity states that it is something a man must prevent a woman from doing.
- **Nature–nurture debate:** if responses to female infidelity were genetic then we would expect all men to behave violently to women, but they do not so there must be an alternative explanation.
- **Anthropomorphism:** evolutionary theories of aggression tend to use human behaviour such as jealousy to explain the animal behaviour.
- **Biological determinism:** evolutionary explanations suggest that aggressive behaviour is instinctive and is 'in our nature'.

Read Item 2 and your textbook.

2 **a** **How do ethologists explain human aggression?**

b Explain what is meant by fixed action pattern behaviour.

c Outline how evolutionary psychologists explain domestic violence.

d Suggest one disadvantage of the evolutionary explanation for human aggression.

Item 3 Social psychology: explanations of aggression

The frustration-aggression hypothesis

The frustration-aggression hypothesis proposes that aggressive behaviour occurs when a person's efforts to attain a goal are frustrated.

Originally there were two hypotheses:
- Frustration leads to some form of aggression.
- Aggression is always the result of frustration.

The revised frustration-aggression hypothesis (Berkowitz 1989) suggests that frustration creates a readiness to respond in an aggressive manner, but that aggression will only happen if environmental cues are present to indicate that an aggressive response is appropriate — if a person becomes frustrated in the presence of a cue to aggression (e.g. a gun) he or she will behave more aggressively.

Research evidence: Berkowitz (1967) 'The aggressive cues hypothesis'

Anger and frustration were caused by the participants' work being criticised by a confederate and then participants were given the opportunity to administer mild electric shocks to the confederate.
- **Condition 1:** cues to aggression are present — a shotgun and revolver were present and the experimenter said 'these must belong to someone else doing an experiment in here'.
- **Condition 2:** no cues to aggression are present — a tennis racket was present.

The rate of electric shocks was higher in the aggressive cues (guns) condition.

Research evidence: Dill and Anderson (1995)

This study looked at the effects of justified and unjustified frustration on aggression. Three groups of participants all performed an origami (folding paper) task that was timed. The participant's success at the origami task was:
- blocked in an unjustified manner
- blocked in a justified manner
- not blocked at all

At a predetermined 'fold' in the timed origami task a confederate, who was 'helping with the research' by pretending to be a participant, asked the experimenter to slow down.
- In **the unjustified group**, the experimenter responds, 'I cannot slow down — my girlfriend/ boyfriend is picking me up after this and I do not want to make them wait.'
- In **the justified condition** the experimenter responds, 'I cannot slow down — my supervisor booked this room for another project afterwards and we must continue.'
- In **the control condition** the experimenter responds, 'Oh, okay I did not realise I was going too quickly, I will slow down.'

Afterwards the participants were asked to complete questionnaires on their levels of aggression and about the ability and likeability of the experimenter. Participants in the unjustified frustration group rated the experimenter as having least ability and as least likeable. The justified frustration group rated the experimenter as less likeable and having less ability than the control group. The results support the hypothesis that frustration can lead to aggression.

Evaluation

- The frustration-aggression hypothesis is useful because it suggests that if, in society, we can prevent or reduce levels of frustration we can also prevent or reduce aggressive behaviour.
- Much of the evidence has low mundane realism, for example students being invited to give electric shocks.
- It ignores differences between people — not everyone who is 'frustrated' will behave aggressively, and the same person may respond differently from one day to the next.
- This is an example of environmental reductionism as it suggests that aggression is simply an unthinking response to a stimulus such as a gun or knife.

Social learning theory

Bandura (1977) states that behaviour is learned from the environment through the process of observational learning. Bandura proposes that humans are active information processors who think about their behaviour and its consequences, and that children learn aggression by observing **role models** whom they then imitate. Children also learn about the consequences of aggression and observe whether there is **positive reinforcement** (through the model achieving what they wanted) or whether aggression is punished. This is known as **direct** or **vicarious reinforcement**.

According to Bandura, factors involving both the model and the learner can play a role in whether social learning is successful:

- **Attention:** if the model or the behaviour is interesting or 'stands out' the child is more likely to pay attention and learn the behaviour.
- **Retention:** the child needs to be able to remember and recall the information about the behaviour observed.
- **Reproduction:** the child needs to be capable of reproducing the behaviour.
- **Motivation:** the child needs to be motivated to imitate the observed behaviour and reinforcement and punishment play an important role in motivation as does vicarious reinforcement.

Research evidence: Bandura, A., Ross, D. and Ross, S. (1961)

Bandura et al. wanted to find out whether aggression can be learned through imitation. In the famous 'Bobo doll' study, Bandura et al. found that children who observed an aggressive role model imitated the models they saw both in terms of specific physical and verbal aggressive acts and in a general increase in aggressive behaviour. They also found a gender effect — boys imitated more physical aggression but not verbal aggression and both boys and girls imitated same-sex models more.

Evaluation

- This theory is useful because it suggests that if, in society, we reduce the amount of modelled aggressive behaviour we can also prevent or reduce aggressive behaviour.
- It is reductionist as it ignores all biological causes of aggressive behaviour.
- It can be criticised as 'soft determinism' as it suggests that children do not have the free will to make 'moral judgements'.

Deindividuation

Deindividuation is the loss of one's sense of identity, usually brought on by being an anonymous member of a group, or by hiding behind a uniform or a mask.

Research evidence: Zimbardo (1971)

In Zimbardo's Stanford prison experiment 24 young, educated, male participants were assigned to the role of either a prisoner or prison guard role in a mock prison. Within 48 hours prisoners became anxious and depressed and Zimbardo suggested they suffered from deindividuation and learned helplessness.

The study had to be stopped on day 6 because the guards lost their normal sense of identity and behaved appallingly towards the prisoners, humiliating them both emotionally and physically. Zimbardo concluded that the guard's extreme and abusive behaviour was due to deindividuation. (For more details on the Stanford prison experiment look at www.lucifereffect.com).

Research evidence: Diener et al. (1976)

In this research a woman placed a bowl of candy in her living room for trick-or-treaters. An observer was placed out of sight in order to record the behaviours of the child trick-or-treaters. The observer recorded whether children came individually or in a group.

- In one condition, the woman asked the children questions such as where they lived and what their name was etc.
- In the other condition, children were completely anonymous.

In each condition, the woman invited the children in, told each child to take only one piece of candy, and then left the room. In 60% of cases, the anonymous 'group' children took more than one piece, sometimes even the entire bowl of candy. This suggests that being an anonymous member of a group does lead to anti-social behaviour.

Read Item 3 and your textbook.

3 a **Outline the original form of the frustration-aggression hypothesis.**

....

....

....

....

....

b Explain what is meant by the 'aggressive cues' hypothesis.

....

....

....

....

....

c Suggest one advantage of the aggressive cues hypothesis.

....

....

....

....

....

....

....

d How does social learning involve cognitive factors?

....

....

....

....

....

....

....

e What happened in stage 2 in the Bandura study of learned aggression?

....

....

....

....

....

....

....

....

f What is meant by the term deindividuation?

....

....

....

....

....

....

....

g In the Zimbardo study, why did deindividuation occur in the prisoners and guards?

....

....

....

....

....

....

....

....

....

....

Item 4 Institutional aggression in the context of prisons

Two theories have been proposed in an attempt to understand why interpersonal violence occurs frequently in prisons — the dispositional explanation (the importation model) and the situational explanation (the deprivation model).

The dispositional explanation: the importation model

This explanation suggests that offenders enter prison with particular characteristics, such as personality traits, values and attitudes, and that these characteristics (dispositional factors) predict they are more likely to engage in interpersonal aggression. According to the dispositional theory, aggression is not a product of the institution but is caused by the characteristics of the individual.

Research evidence

Keller and Wang (2005) found that prison violence is more likely to occur in facilities that hold troublesome inmates. Poole and Regoli (1983) studied juvenile offenders in four different institutions, and found that pre-institutional violence was the best predictor of inmate aggression.

Evaluation

- The dispositional model does not suggest how to reduce violent behaviour in prisons.
- The suggestion that aggression is caused by nature rather than nurture ignores the environmental situation of the inmates and is thus a reductionist explanation.
- In research into institutional aggression within prisons there is a gender bias as it is only the behaviour of men which is analysed and therefore researchers take an androcentric (male-based) view of aggression.

The situational explanation: the deprivation model

The situational explanation (the deprivation model) suggests that it is the situational factors of the prison that cause aggression. For example, overcrowding is linked to an increase in interpersonal violence, self-harm and suicide. The Stanford prison experiment by Zimbardo supports the situational explanation.

Research evidence

Bandura et al. (1975) studied participants who were told they were working on a task with students from another school. In one condition, participants overheard an assistant refer to the students 'from the other school' as 'animals' while in another condition, they were referred to as 'nice'. When the participants were asked to deliver what they believed to be real electric shocks, higher shocks were delivered in the 'animals' condition. This provides support for Zimbardo's belief in the effect of dehumanising labels.

Evaluation

Zimbardo's explanation of institutional aggression is useful as it has real-life relevance. Zimbardo (2007) claims that the same social psychological processes found in the Stanford prison experiment occurred during the abuse of Iraqi prisoners at Abu Ghraib prison in Iraq.

Read Item 4 and your textbook.

4 **a** **In terms of aggression in prisons, what is meant by the dispositional explanation?**

b **In terms of aggression in prisons, why is the situational explanation useful?**

c McCorkle et al. (1995) studied 371 prisons in the USA and found little evidence to support the connection between violence and factors such as overcrowding. Why does this evidence undermine the situational explanation of prison violence?

....

....

....

....

....

....

....

....

....

....

....

Item 5 Media influences on aggression

Huesmann and Eron et al. found that children who had watched many hours of television violence when they were 8 years old were more likely to be arrested and prosecuted for criminal acts as adults.

The effects of computer games

As many as 97% of adolescents aged 12–17 play video games. A survey in 2008 found that half of all teens who reported playing video games played every day for an hour or more. Many of the most popular video games, such as 'Grand Theft Auto', are violent and several meta-analytic reviews have reported negative effects of exposure to violence in video games.

Huesmann and Moiser (1996) suggest three ways that exposure to media violence may lead to aggression in children:

- observational learning and imitation
- cognitive priming
- desensitisation

Research evidence

Anderson et al. (2010) concluded that 'the evidence strongly suggests that exposure to violent video games is a causal risk factor for increased aggressive behaviour, aggressive cognition, and aggressive affect and for decreased empathy and prosocial behaviour'.

Observational learning: social learning theory

Hint: Revise the Bobo doll study by Bandura, Ross and Ross.

Children observe the behaviour of media models and may then imitate that behaviour, especially when the child admires or identifies themselves with the person on television. Television may also inform viewers of the positive and negative consequences of violent behaviour. The more children believe that they are like the characters, the more likely they are to try to copy the observed behaviour.

Cognitive priming

Cognitive priming refers to the activation of existing aggressive thoughts and feelings and explains why children observe one kind of aggressive behaviour on television but carry out a different aggressive act afterwards. The theory suggests that immediately after watching a violent programme the viewer is primed to respond aggressively because a network of aggressive memories has been retrieved. Also that frequent exposure to violent scenes may cause children to store cognitive scripts for aggressive behaviour which may be recalled later in similar situations.

Research evidence

Josephson (1987) studied a sample of 396 boys who were ice hockey players. The boys were split into two groups. Before a game, Group 1 watched a violent film and Group 2 watched a non-violent film. Impartial observers rated aggressiveness in the game. Those who saw the violent film behaved more aggressively (e.g. tripping and shoving other players).

Desensitisation (disinhibition)

This theory suggests that repeated exposure to violence in the media 'desensitised' people to violence and because people become 'used to it' (habituated) it has less impact on them. This theory also suggests that people who watch a lot of violent television become less anxious about violence. As a result of desensitisation they do not react to violence in the same way.

Evaluation of media influences on aggression

Research has usually focused on male-on-male violence, frequently done in artificial experiments using unrepresentative samples (e.g. male students). Also, there are methodological problems to overcome, such as ethical issues, in laboratory experiments, lack of ecological validity and in correlation lack of cause and effect.

Read Item 5 and your textbook.

5 **a** **If there is a correlation between watching television violence as a child and aggressive behaviour as an adult why can we not say that watching television violence causes adult aggression?**

....

....

....

....

....

....

b **What is meant by 'cognitive priming'?**

....

....

....

....

....

c **Give one reason why children who play violent video games may behave more aggressively.**

....

....

....

....

....

....

d In terms of aggressive behaviour, how might playing violent video games desensitise a person to aggression?

....

....

....

....

....

....

....

....

....

....

....

....

....

Exam-style questions

6 a Which one of the following is NOT a neural or a hormonal mechanism in aggression?

1 mark

Circle the letter of the answer that you think is correct.

A The hypothalamus

B Serotonin

C Gender

D The amygdala

b Briefly outline the function of the MAO-A gene.

2 marks

....

....

....

....

....

c   Which one of the following list is NOT true of ethological explanations for aggressive behaviours?

Circle the letter of the answer that you think is correct.

A   Are instinctive

B   Are species specific

C   Are learned

D   Are adaptive

d   Briefly outline one evolutionary explanation for male aggressive behaviour.   **2 marks**

....

....

....

....

....

....

....

....

....

....

e   Explain how playing violent video games may cause aggressive behaviour in children. Support your explanation with psychological evidence.   **4 marks**

....

....

....

....

....

....

....

....

....

....

....

....

....

....

f Discuss evolutionary explanations for human aggression. (8 marks)

g Evaluate the social learning theory of human aggression. (8 marks) h   A psychologist carried out a study of 10 boys who said they played violent computer games for at least 2 hours every day (Group A), and another 10 boys who said they never played any violent computer games (Group B). Each of the boys was observed in their school playground for 1 hour on Friday lunchtime and the total number of aggressive behaviours they demonstrated was recorded. The data collected are given in the table below.

The effects of playing violent computer games on aggressive behaviour

Boy	Number of aggressive acts	
	Group A	Group B
1	10	5
2	7	2
3	3	6
4	5	5
5	12	8
6	6	4
7	5	9
8	6	11
9	8	10
10	26	12
Mean	8.8	6.3
Median	6.5	5.5

i   In this study, which is the most appropriate measure of central tendency? Explain your answer.

2 marks

ii   Calculate the range for the two groups. What does the range tell us about the effect of playing violent computer games?

4 marks

h

iii **The researchers concluded that playing violent video games caused the boys to behave aggressively in the playground. Explain whether or not you think this is a valid conclusion.**

4 marks

iv **Briefly explain one limitation of the dispositional explanation for institutional aggression.**

2 marks

Hodder Education, an Hachette UK company, Carmelite House 50 Victoria Embankment, London EC4Y 0DZ

Orders

Bookpoint Ltd, 130 Park Drive, Milton Park, Abingdon, Oxfordshire OX14 4SB

tel: 01235 827827

fax: 01235 400401

e-mail: education@bookpoint.co.uk

Lines are open 9.00 a.m.–5.00 p.m., Monday to Saturday, with a 24-hour message answering service. You can also order through the Hodder Education website: www.hoddereducation.co.uk

© Molly Marshall 2016

ISBN 978-1-4718-4519-2

First printed 2016

Impression number   6   5   4   3

Year   2021   2020   2019   2018

This guide has been written specifically to support students preparing for the AQA A-level Psychology examinations. The content has been neither approved nor endorsed by AQA and remains the sole responsibility of the author.

Typeset by Aptara, India

Printed in Dubai

Hachette UK's policy is to use papers that are natural, renewable and recyclable products and made from wood grown in sustainable forests. The logging and manufacturing processes are expected to conform to the environmental regulations of the country of origin.

ISBN 978-1-4718-4519-2